$$+2 +3 +4 +5$$
$$+4 +3 +2 +1$$
$$\overline{+6 +6 +6 +6}$$

A Number Tric

By Ali R. Amir-Moez

$$+5$$
$$+1$$
$$\overline{+6}$$

"What are you doing here, Carl?" asked the teacher. "You should be doing the problem I gave you."

"I have finished it, sir," said Carl.

The teacher was astonished to find that Carl's answer was right. That day the teacher had had much to do, and had given a long problem to his young students, hoping to keep them busy for the whole hour. The problem wasn't difficult. It was just one that would take a lot of time. The teacher had told his pupils to find the sum of all the numbers from 1 through 100. He thought that it would keep them busy for an hour, considering all the mistakes and checking.

Carl had gone as far as

$$1 + 2 + 3 + 4 + 5 = 15$$

when he suddenly saw a short cut. He noticed that if he wrote this sum backward under itself, and added each column, he would get:

$$1 + 2 + 3 + 4 + 5$$
$$5 + 4 + 3 + 2 + 1$$
$$\overline{6 + 6 + 6 + 6 + 6}$$

Then, instead of adding $1 + 2 + 3 + 4 + 5$, he wrote:

$$1 + 5 = 6$$

And, since there were five numbers:

$$5 \times 6 = 30$$

Since 30 was twice the correct answer, he wrote

$$30 \div 2 = 15$$

Why couldn't he use the same trick for adding 1 through 100? He tried it:

$$1 + 100 = 101$$

Then, since there were one hundred numbers:

$$100 \times 101 = 10100$$

Finally the answer was:

$$10100 \div 2 = 5050$$

"This is right!" said the teacher. "How did you do it so soon?"

"Simple," answered Carl, and explained his trick.

Carl Friedrich Gauss, the son of a day laborer, was born in Braunschweig, Germany, in 1777. He grew up as a boy who loved to play with numbers. The news of his genius got to the Duke of Braunschweig. The Duke supported his education at Göttingen University. Carl became one of Germany's great mathematicians. His pet subject was "number theory," which means the study of the beauty of numbers. And he also made important discoveries in astronomy and physics.

When you study physics in college, you will learn that we honor Carl by calling the unit of magnetic force a "gauss."

But right today you will have more fun with the trick of numbers which Carl discovered when he was just about your age. Try his trick on some other series of numbers like 1 through 20, or 1 through 36, just to make sure you can do it.

1

Here are some fun facts about numbers. These are ways to make numbers come out in pyramids. Try them for yourself.

Number Pyramids By Ali R. Amir-Moez

An Addition Pyramid

$$1 = 1 \times 1$$
$$1 + 2 + 1 = 2 \times 2$$
$$1 + 2 + 3 + 2 + 1 = 3 \times 3$$

(You write the next line.)

A Multiplication Pyramid

$$1 \times 1 = 1$$
$$11 \times 11 = 121$$
$$111 \times 111 = 12321$$
$$1111 \times 1111 = 1234321$$

(You write the next line.)

A Combination Pyramid

$$(1 \times 9) + 2 = 11$$
$$(12 \times 9) + 3 = 111$$
$$(123 \times 9) + 4 =$$
$$(1234 \times 9) + 5 =$$
$$(12345 \times 9) + 6 =$$

(You finish the last pyramid.)

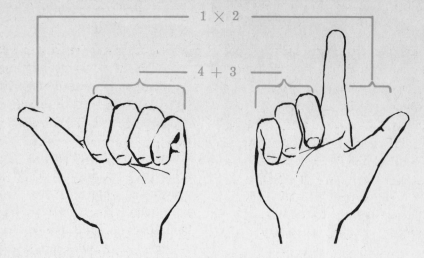

Fingers for Multiplication

By Ali R. Amir-Moez and G. R. Musser

When you were very young, you may have used your fingers to help with adding numbers. Here is a trick in which fingers help check multiplication. However, this trick only works for multiplication of numbers from 6 through 10. And one must know the multiplication tables of 1 through 5. We shall consider the thumb as the fifth finger, thus having ten fingers with which to work.

In multiplication, there is the multiplicand and the multiplier, the two numbers which are to be multiplied. From each of these, subtract 5. For instance, if you are multiplying 9×8, subtract 5 from each and get 4×3.

Now use your fingers. Bend down 4 fingers of your left hand and 3 fingers of your right hand. **Add the number of bent fingers** of the left hand to the bent fingers of the right hand to get the number for the tens column of the answer.

In this case it is 7 or 70.

$$4 + 3 = 7$$

Multiply the number of straight fingers of the left hand by the number of straight fingers of the right hand for the number to be placed in the ones column of the answer. In this case it is 2.

$$1 \times 2 = 2$$

Therefore, the product of 9×8 is 72!

If the multiplication of the straight fingers comes out more than 9, add the product of the straight fingers to the sum of the bent fingers for your final answer. Such is the case in this example: $6 \times 6 = ?$ Bend down 1 finger on each hand. Add the bent fingers.

$$1 + 1 = 2$$

The figure 2 will go in the tens column, giving 20.

Multiply the straight fingers.

$$4 \times 4 = 16$$

The product is a two-digit figure. Therefore, add the product and the sum to get the final answer.

$$20 + 16 = 36$$

This checks the original problem of $6 \times 6 = 36$.

Ancient Multiplication

By Ali R. Amir-Moez

More than thirty-five hundred years ago Egyptians discovered some interesting ways of multiplication. Here is a different way which you may never have thought of.

Suppose you had the problem: Multiply $13 \times 12 = ?$

Draw a line separating two columns. In the column on the left, begin with the number 1, double it and write 2, double that and write 4, and so on. In the column at the right, put the number you are multiplying by (in this case, the number 12). Under the 12, double it and write 24, double 24 and write the number 48 under that, and so on.

Multiply $13 \times 12 = ?$

1	12
2	24
4	48
8	96
16	192

Now find the numbers in the left column which, when added together, total 13. The numbers $1 + 4 + 8 = 13$, so underline the numbers in the right column opposite these numbers. Then add these numbers ($12 + 48 + 96$) together and you will get the sum 156, which is the answer when you multiply 13×12.

Now let us try another example. Multiply $38 \times 251 = ?$

1	251
2	502
4	1004
8	2008
16	4016
32	8032

We see that $2 + 4 + 32 = 38$. So $38 \times 251 = 502 + 1004 + 8032 = 9538$.

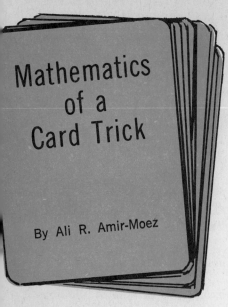

Mathematics of a Card Trick

By Ali R. Amir-Moez

Make ten cards and number them from 1 to 10. Place them in a pile in the following order from bottom to top: 5, 9, 4, 7, 3, 10, 2, 6, 1, 8.

Hold the pile in your hand without disturbing the order. Put the top card on the bottom of the pile. The next card will be 1. Place it on the table. Again put the top card on the bottom of the pile, and the next card, 2, on the table. Continue this till all the cards are on the table in proper order from 1 to 10.

What we have done is to put the cards in a certain order so we can do the trick. How this order is arrived at might itself be called a mathematical trick. We simply do the original trick backwards, in this manner:

First arrange the cards in a pile from 1 to 10, bottom to top. Put the pile on the table. Pick up the top card. Then pick up the next card and put it on top of the card in your hand. Put the bottom card in your hand on top of the other card in your hand. Pick up the next card from the pile, put it on top of the cards in your hand, and again put the bottom card on top. Continue like this till all the cards are picked up. They will be piled in the order suggested for the trick.

We now have a mathematical generalization or "method of ordering." When we want to arrange or "order" cards for a trick, we simply do the trick backwards.

Now see if you can answer the following questions, using this method of ordering. You will, of course, need many more than ten cards.

1. Is it possible to do the trick with more than ten cards?

2. Is it possible each time to put two cards under instead of one, and do the trick?

3. How about putting three cards under each time, or perhaps more?

4. Is it possible to put one card under and one card down the first time, two under and two down the second time, and three under and three down the third time, and so on?

There are many more questions that can be asked. Why don't you ask more and answer them?

Multiplication With Fingers

By Ali R. Amir-Moez and G. R. Musser

This is a trick in which multiplication can be done on your fingers as a quick check for the multiplication you have done in your head. To multiply by 9, stretch out your hands on a table so that you can see the backs of all ten fingers. Now pick out a number from the set 1, 2, 3, 4, 5, 6, 7, 8, 9, 10 which you wish to multiply by 9. If you pick 4, bend the fourth finger, counting from the left. There are three fingers at the left of the bent finger and 6 fingers at the right of the bent finger. The answer is 36.

$$9 \times 4 = 36$$

Let's try it again. If you pick 7 to be multiplied by 9, count from the left and bend under the seventh finger. It works again and tells you

$$9 \times 7 = 63$$

Indeed, 9 x 10 can be tested. Bending down the tenth finger from the left, there are 9 fingers at the left of the bent finger and 0 fingers at the right. So the answer is 90.

You will notice that for multiplication by 9, we use 9 + 1 or 10 fingers. We are doing arithmetic in base 10. The number of fingers at the left of the bent finger was multiplied by 10 and added to the number of fingers at the right of the bent finger.

This same principle can be used to check multiplication by other numbers. If we work with base 8, we will use 8 fingers and be multiplying by 7, using the set 1, 2, 3, 4, 5, 6, 7, 8. It may help to hold your hands at the edge of a table in such a way that only the fingers you are actually using for the trick are in sight on top of the table, the others being tucked underneath the table.

An example is 7 x 6 = ? We will bend down the sixth finger, leaving 5 fingers at the left of the bent finger and 2 fingers at the right of the bent finger. The number at the left is multiplied by 8 and added to the number at the right.

$$5 \times 8 = 40$$
$$40 + 2 = 42$$

And this checks with 6 x 7 = 42.

Try checking all your multiplication problems by this quick and easy method.

3

Fun With Triangles

By Ali R. Amir-Moez

Where is the center of a triangle? How can such an irregular figure have a center?

Any triangle does have a special kind of center which is called its **center of gravity.** You might think of it this way. If you were to cut a triangle out of paper or cardboard, where is the point at which you would stick a pin to balance it? Of course you can find out by just trying different points. But here is a simple and foolproof way.

On a piece of heavy paper draw a large triangle. Make it any shape you wish. Label its three points **a, b,** and **c** as in Figure 1. Cut out the triangle with scissors.

Now find the middle point (midpoint) on each of the three sides. Fold point **a** over to match point **b** and make a little crease which will be the exact middle of the side **ab.** Make a pencil mark on the crease at the edge. Repeat this for the other sides **bc** and **ac.** Then smooth out the creases.

Draw a straight line from each point of the triangle to the midpoint of the opposite side. Of course these lines must cross each other. But notice that all three cross at one point! They will always do this, no matter how you draw the triangle. Label the cross-point **o** as in Figure 2.

There must be something special about point **o.** Let's try and see. Slightly prick the triangle with a pin at point **o.** Now see if you can balance the paper triangle on the

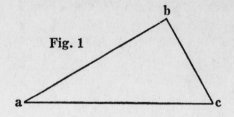

Fig. 1

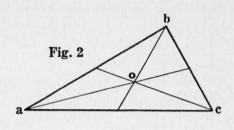

Fig. 2

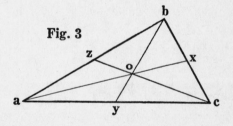

Fig. 3

pin at this point. Is there any other point at which the triangle will balance? You have found out that **o** is the point of balance or the center of gravity of your triangle.

You have learned a trick that works for all triangles. I dare you to find a triangle of any shape for which the trick won't work.

If you look at your triangles you may notice something else. I can show you best if you label the midpoints of the sides x, y, and z as in Figure 3. Look at the line which goes from **a** to **o** to x. The distance from **a** to **o** is just exactly twice as long as the distance from **o** to x. And the same thing is true for each of the other lines through **o.** But don't just take my word. Find a way to fold your triangles to see if I am right.

Something Amazing

Have a friend select a page in a book, choose a word in any one of the first nine lines and in the first nine words of that line. Tell him you can find the word chosen.

Ask him to multiply the number of the page by 2, and then by 5; then to add 20; next add the number of the line, add 5 to that sum, and multiply by 10; finally to add the number of the word in the line, and to give you the result. From the number he gives you subtract 250, in your mind, and you can open the book to the page of the line and show him the word he selected.

Example:
page 124, 1st line, 7th word
$124 \times 2 = 248$
$248 \times 5 = 1240 + 20 = 1260$
$1260 + 1 = 1261 + 5 = 1266$
$1266 \times 10 = 12660 + 7 = 12667$
$12667 - 250 = 12417$

Strange But True
By Ali R. Amir-Moez

Let's play with a triangle. I guess you know that a triangle is a three-sided flat figure. Cut a triangle of any size or shape out of a piece of paper, Figure 1. Be sure to cut it carefully. Find the middle of each side by putting the two ends of each side together carefully, and folding that side. The crease is exactly the middle of that side, Figure 2. Now use your pencil and mark each crease.

If you draw lines connecting the middles of the three sides, you will get four triangles. Let us number them, 1, 2, 3, and 4, Figure 3. These triangles are of the same size. We test it by cutting them from one another, Figure 4. Now we see that 1, 2, and 3 fit one over another precisely, but you have to twist the triangle 4 upside down to make it fit over the others, Figure 5. Try this a few times with different size and shape triangles. It works every time. It is strange but true.

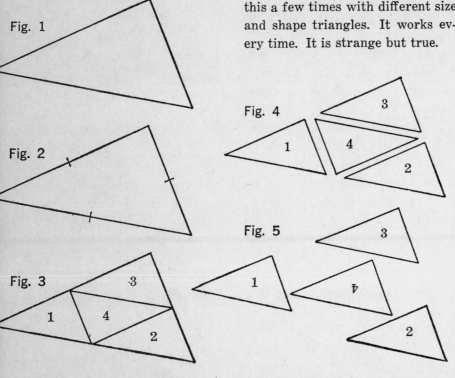

Fig. 1

Fig. 2

Fig. 3

Fig. 4

Fig. 5

"My mom wants me to be a nuclear physicist. My pop wants me to be an electronics engineer, and I want to pass arithmetic."

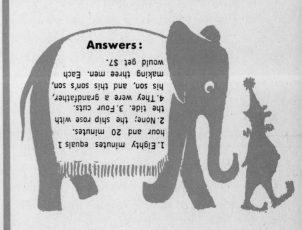

SCHOOL

TRICKS AND TEASERS

1. Walking from his house to the store, Cy takes 1 hour and 20 minutes. Returning to his home at the same speed, it takes him 80 minutes. How could this be?

2. The ladder on a ship in the harbor had ten rungs, a foot apart. The bottom rung touched the water at low tide. When the tide rose three feet, how many of the rungs of the ladder were under water?

3. A certain pole is 10 feet long. If you sawed it into five pieces, each 2 feet long, how many times would you cut it?

4. How may two fathers and two sons divide twenty-one one-dollar bills evenly among themselves, without making change?

Answers:

1. Eighty minutes equals 1 hour and 20 minutes. 2. None; the ship rose with the tide. 3. Four cuts. 4. They were a grandfather, his son, and this son's son, making three men. Each would get $7.

5

More Fun With Triangles

By Ali R. Amir-Moez

Here's another trick of a triangle. Let's start by drawing a large triangle on a piece of paper. Make it any shape you wish. Label the corners of the triangle A, B, and C as in Figure 1. We have also labeled each of the sides. We can say that side AB is the line which connects corner A to corner B.

Cut out the triangle with scissors.

Now find the midpoints of the sides AB and AC. Fold point A over point B, and make a little crease at the center of side AB. Mark it with a pencil at the edge. Repeat this to mark the center of side AC. You have two new points. Label them M and N, and draw a straight line between them as in Figure 2.

You have made a new triangle which has corners at A, M, and N. With a pencil, shade in this new triangle AMN. Notice that the shaded triangle is rather specially like the big triangle ABC.

Cut with scissors to separate the shaded triangle as in Figure 3. Now let's see how special the shaded triangle really is.

First you will find that the line BC of the large triangle is twice as long as the line MN of the shaded triangle. Carefully fold points B and C together to divide the length BC in half, and then put MN over it to test.

Next you can compare the corners of the shaded triangle and the larger triangle from which it was cut. Notice that corner M fits perfectly over corner B. Corner N

fits perfectly over corner C. You see how the shaded triangle AMN is specially like the larger triangle ABC from which you cut it. The two triangles are alike in the size of their corners.

Let's stop and think about the corners of a triangle. There are always three of them, just as there are three lines for the sides. Whenever lines come together, they make an angle between them. A **triangle** is so named because it has three angles inside its three corners.

There is still one more thing that is special about our way of cutting up the large triangle. Look at the upper corners or angles of the large piece, as in Figure 4. Label these P and Q.

Cut off corner P. Fit it together with corner M as in Figure 5. The two corners fit together to make a straight line. Of course they had to fit this way. They made a straight line as in Figure 2 before you cut them apart. Now try to fit corner P to corner B as in Figure 6. They also fit together to make a straight line. You can discover the same things about corner Q fitted to corner N or corner C.

By fitting corners or angles together, you have shown that there is also something special about the lines MN and BC of Figure 2. They are called parallel lines. Someday you will discover that you actually proved that these lines are parallel. Then you will be studying geometry. Right now you are just having fun.

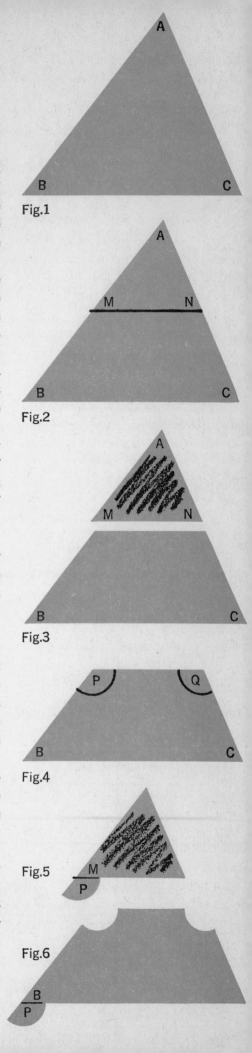

Fig.1

Fig.2

Fig.3

Fig.4

Fig.5

Fig.6

6

Fun With a Special Triangle   By Ali R. Amir-Moez

Whenever two straight lines come together they make an **angle**. As you will see in Figure 1, the sides of an angle may be squeezed almost shut or open up wide. There is one special kind which is called a **right angle**. It is special because, if we fit two right angles with their corners together, we get a straight line as in Figure 2.

If we draw a triangle with a right angle for one of its corners, we get a special and interesting figure. It is called a **right triangle**.

An easy way to get a right triangle is to use the corner of a sheet of paper. Draw a straight line anywhere across the corner as in Figure 3 and cut along the line. Label the right angle A and the other two angles B and C.

The first interesting fact is that the two angles B and C together always fit exactly into the right angle A. Try this by cutting off the B and C corners and fitting them as in Figure 4.

To discover a second interesting fact, we need to cut out another right triangle as we did in Figure 3. The side BC opposite the right angle is special, too, and it has a fancy name. It is the **hypotenuse**. Fold the corners at B and C together and make a little crease at the center of the hypotenuse. Make a pencil mark at the edge of the crease and label it M. Draw in the line AM as in Figure 5.

We now have cut our right triangle into two new triangles which look rather interesting and special. In order to see how special they are, shade the upper triangle with a pencil and cut them apart along AM as in Figure 5.

Notice that your cut divided the right angle A into two pieces. By folding the shaded triangle we can see that one part of angle A is the same size as angle B. By folding the lower triangle we can see that the other part of angle A is the same size as angle C. What can you discover about the lengths of two sides of each of our two new triangles?

Now let me slip in two questions, and you do the work. Cut a new right triangle as we did in Figure 3. Look at what we did in Figure 4 and what we did in Figure 5. Can you find a way to fold a right triangle to do both things at once?

And here is the second question. No triangle can have more than one corner that is a right angle. Why is this?

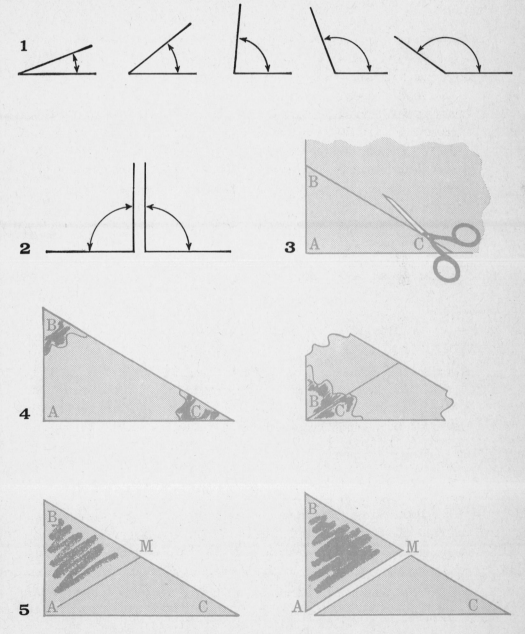

A Triangle Surprise

By Ali R. Amir-Moez

Here is an interesting experiment with triangles—three-sided figures. Three are shown.

Choose one shape. Cut a figure like it from paper. Make it larger than the figure shown.

Mark the corners, A, B, and C, as in Figure 1. The paper triangle is to be cut in three pieces as shown by the dotted lines. The three letters will be on the original corners.

No matter what size or shape triangle we choose, we see that the three corners (angles) A, B, C, fit together on a straight line as in Figure 2. The corners A, B, and C can be put together in any order, and this is true.

Experiment with other triangle shapes. Two others are shown.

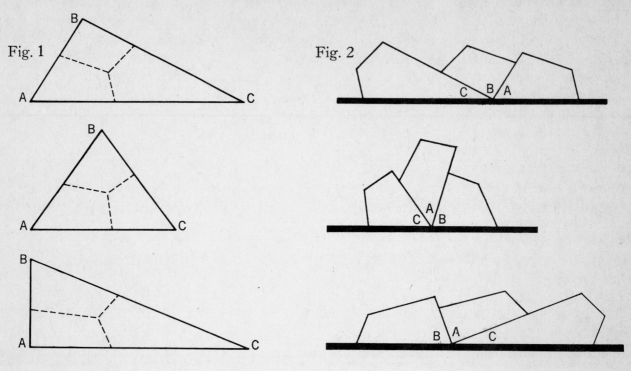

Fig. 1

Fig. 2

8

By C. Margaret Schofer

Make fifteen cards of lightweight cardboard, 2½ by 2½ inches.

On three cards print clearly, and quite large, the number 1. On three, print 2. On three, print 3. On three, print 4. And on three, print STUNG AGAIN.

Shuffle the cards well, then lay them out, face down, in a horizontal row of five piles, three cards in each pile.

To play, always start with Pile No. 5, Turn over the top card. If it is a 1, place it, face up, under Pile No. 1. If it is a 2, place it under Pile No. 2, and so on. If it is STUNG AGAIN, place it under Pile No. 5. Then turn over the top card of whatever pile you placed the card under, and place it face up under the proper pile.

Continue in this manner as long as you can.

To win the game you must get all the numbers in their proper piles, face up, before you get the three STUNG AGAINS face up. When you get three STUNG AGAINS face up, you have no card on top to turn over so you cannot continue play. In other words — you are STUNG AGAIN!

It Seems Like Magic

By Ali R. Amir-Moez

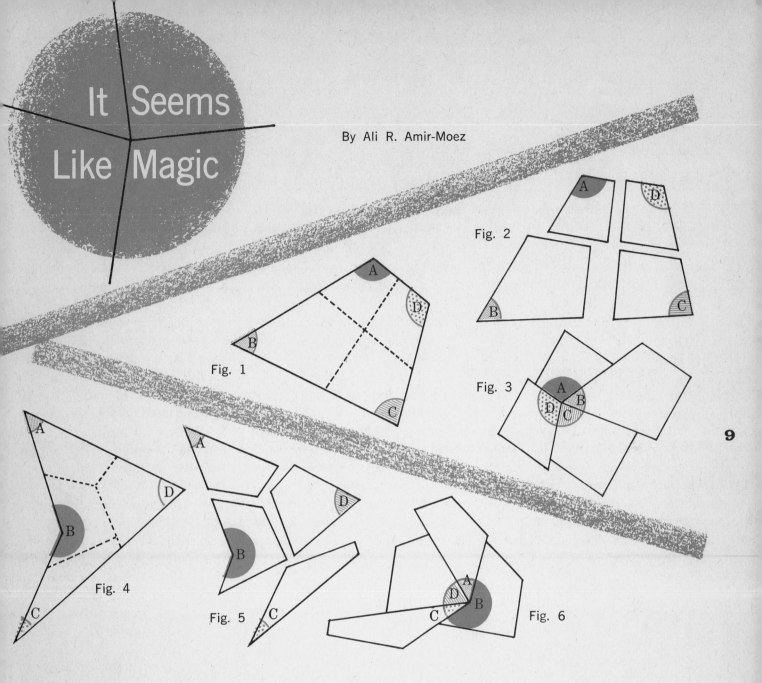

Fig. 1

Fig. 2

Fig. 3

Fig. 4

Fig. 5

Fig. 6

9

It's interesting to experiment with four-sided figures. Their big name is quadrilateral or quadrangle.

Suppose we letter a quadrilateral A, B, C, D, Figure 1. As we see it in Figure 1, we do not have to have all sides equal. Let us cut a piece of paper like Figure 1. It is better to choose a larger figure. Then we cut the quadrilateral into four pieces through the dotted lines and we get four pieces as in Figure 2.

The experiment is as follows: No matter what size or shape quadrilateral we choose, we see that the four corners (angles) A, B, C,

and D fit together once around as in Figure 3. The corners A, B, C, and D can be put together in any order, and this fact is true.

This property does not belong only to a convex quadrilateral such as in Figure 1. We shall experiment with a nonconvex quadrangle like Figure 4. We cut a piece of paper like Figure 4, and then we cut it along the dotted lines, and we get four pieces as in Figure 5. These four pieces also fit together once around as in Figure 6. We also observe that the order is not important.

Exterior Angles

By Ali R. Amir-Moez

Let's make a puzzle from a stuck-out triangle.

With a ruler, draw a triangle on a sheet of paper. As in Figure 1, extend the sides of the triangle so that the three lines cross and go on to the edges of the paper. Don't try to make a regular triangle. The whole idea is that just any old triangle will do, if it is made from three straight lines.

The way to finish the puzzle is shown in Figure 1. Look at the three crosspoints which also make the corners of the triangle. Draw a rough circle around each of these. Inside the three crosspoints are the three inside angles of the triangle. Label them A, B, and C. Notice that opposite A and outside the triangle there is another angle which looks just the same size. Label it A also. In the same way label the outside B and C angles. With a pencil, shade over the outside A, B, and C so that we can tell them apart from the inside angles.

The circle around the A angles also contains another pair of angles. Label each of these X. Likewise we will get another pair of Y angles between the B's, and a pair of Z angles between the C's. Use some other kind of pencil marks or colored shading on one X and one Y and one Z. Our work of art should look about like Figure 1.

With scissors, carefully cut along each of the straight lines from one edge of the paper to the other. This will give us the pieces of paper which make up our puzzle.

Our first job is to put the pieces back together just as they were before we cut them apart. Notice that at each of the three cross-points the marked angles fit together to make half the complete circle. By matching on top of each other, you can see that each shaded angle is just the same size as its opposite unshaded angle.

The idea of our puzzle is that there are other ways of fitting together our marked angles. The shaded X, Y, and Z will fit together around a circle as in Figure 2. The shaded A, B, and C will fit together half around a circle as in Figure 3. You can already guess what will happen if we could fit the unshaded A, B, and C points of the triangle, or what would happen if we fitted together the unshaded X, Y, and Z.

There is still more we can do. It turns out that we can neatly fit a B and a C right on top of an X as in Figure 4. What two angles would we expect to fit over a Y? What two angles fit over a Z?

No matter how you draw your triangle, your puzzle will always do all of these things. So the real puzzle is: Why should it be so?

10

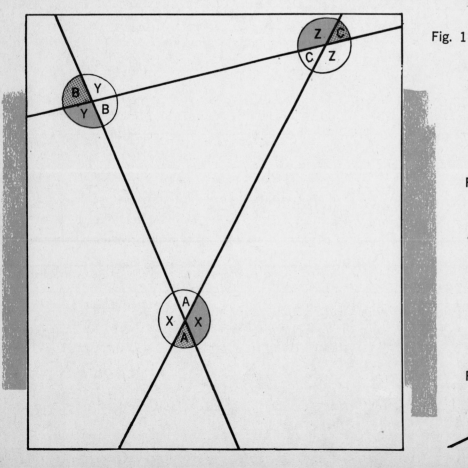

Fig. 1

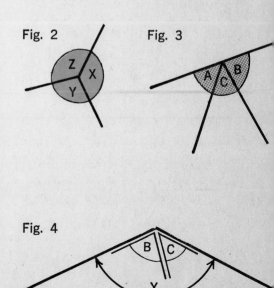

Fig. 2   Fig. 3

Fig. 4

Trisect a Right Angle

By Ali R. Amir-Moez

In geometry there are some problems which became famous because no one could solve them. For many of these it has even been possible to prove that they cannot be solved. Perhaps the most famous one is the angle-trisection, which means dividing an angle into three exactly equal parts. For most angles this is impossible, if we work in the usual way of geometry, using only straight lines and circles.

There is a special angle which we can easily divide into three equal parts. We can trisect a right angle. Let's do it.

Everyone knows that a corner of a sheet of paper is a right angle. Fold a sheet of paper in half lengthwise to get a crease right in the middle of the paper. Let us call this creased line PQ. Use one corner of the paper as your right angle as in Figure 1. Call this corner A, and the other two corners B and C as shown.

Put corner B on line PQ and crease as in Figure 1. Call the creased line AK. Unfold the paper.

Fold line AC over to the creased line AK as in Figure 2, and crease. Call this new creased line AH.

Unfold the paper. It should look like Figure 3.

At the corner A we have three angles. The first one is between the lines AB and AK. The second one is between the lines AK and AH. The third one is between the lines AH and AC. If you have made your folds carefully, these three angles will be exactly equal. Now your job is to test the angles to find out if this is true.

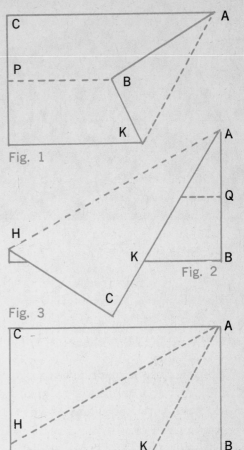

Fig. 1

Fig. 2

Fig. 3

11

At the left, look at the square above the circle. Find at the right the two pieces which you put together to make it. Do the same for the other two figures at the left.

This picture contains the numbers 1 through 10. Can you find them?

Which of these have four corners like the corner of a carpenter's square?
Which has two such corners?
Which has one such corner?
Which have no such corners?

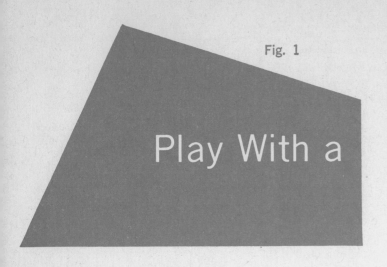

Fig. 1

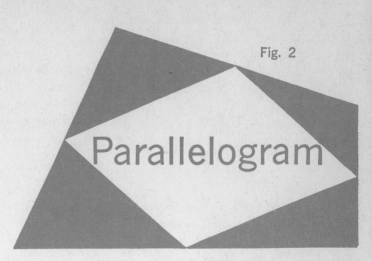

Fig. 2

Play With a Parallelogram

By Ali R. Amir-Moez

We have played with a three-sided figure — the triangle. What about a four-sided figure? Just like every animal in a zoo, every kind of figure has a name. A flat four-sided figure is a **quadrilateral.**

Let's begin by drawing a quadrilateral with pencil and ruler. I have drawn one in Figure 1. You can draw yours any way you wish. Draw a lot of them just to see how different they can be. The only requirement is that each must have four sides, and four angles or corners.

Out of any old quadrilateral we can make a special kind. Let's make it first and then name it. Start with any one of the four-sided figures you have drawn. Cut it out with scissors. Find the middle point of one side by bringing together the corners and making

a little crease at the center. Repeat this for the other three sides. Mark each midpoint with a pencil at the edge of the paper. Now draw straight lines to connect these four points as in Figure 2.

Our lines have made a new quadrilateral which looks rather special. It is a **parallelogram.** Cut it out with scissors. Let's see what is special about it.

We want to look at the corners or angles of our parallelogram. Pick any two opposite angles and shade them with a pencil. Label them A and B as in Figure 3. Label the other two angles C and D. Then cut off two of the corners next to each other such as B and D.

If we put shaded corner B on top of the opposite corner A we see that it exactly fits. These two angles have the same size. If we match the two unshaded angles we

find they also are equal in size. This is true of any parallelogram: Opposite angles are equal.

We should also see what we can do with shaded corner B and unshaded corner D. They fit together on one side to make a straight line as in Figure 4. What about corners A and D? What about corners C and B? We see a second fact about a parallelogram: Any two angles next to each other will add together to make a straight line.

What we have done works because of still another fact about a parallelogram. Any two opposite sides are parallel — like the rails of a railroad track. No matter how far we extend the sides as in Figure 5, they never come together.

Now you know why we call a parallelogram a parallelogram.

12

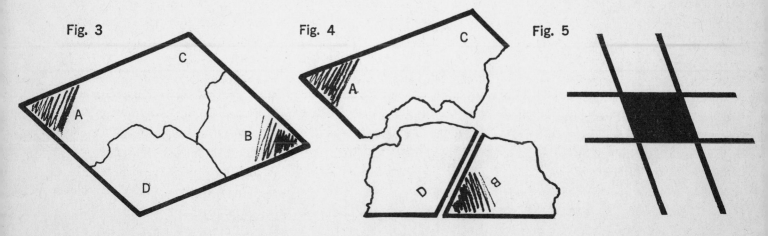

Fig. 3

Fig. 4

Fig. 5

Fig. 3

More Fun

Fig. 1

By Ali R. Amir-Moez

With a Parallelogram

Fig. 2

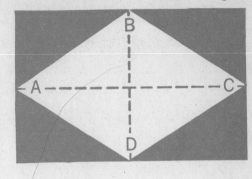

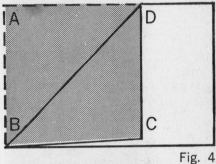

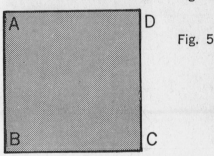

Fig. 4

Fig. 5

13

We have found that a **parallelogram** is a special kind of **quadrilateral** or four-sided figure. We can make parallelograms in many different shapes. One is shown in Figure 1. There are also some special kinds of parallelograms.

Suppose we ask about a parallelogram in which all four angles are equal. Where would we find such a figure? Look at a sheet of paper. It is a parallelogram. Cut off any one of the corners and fit it over each of the other three corners. We find that the angles at all four corners are equal. What kind of an angle will do this? There is only one. Perhaps you remember that it is a **right angle.**

In Figure 2 we see the special kind of parallelogram shaped like a sheet of paper. It has equal angles (and right angles) at all four corners. It is called a **rectangle.**

Suppose we ask about a parallelogram in which all four sides are equal in length. Let's make one from a sheet of paper. Find the middle of each side by folding corners together and making a little crease. With a pencil, mark the midpoint of each edge. Connect the midpoints with lines as in Figure 3. We have a new and special parallelogram, ABCD. Cut it out with scissors. Just by folding along the lines BD and AC we can see that all the sides are equal in length. But how about the angles? Cut one out and compare with the others. The angles at A and C are equal but they are not the same as the angles at B and D.

Our second special kind of parallelogram has four equal sides. Most people would call it a diamond. You might like to call it by its other name. It is a **rhombus.**

Can we make a figure which will have four equal sides and also four equal angles? I think you know the answer, but let's make one, anyway. Take a new sheet of paper. As in Figure 4 fold corner A down to the long side so that the edges of the paper come together. Make a crease in the paper. The crease will run from corner B

to a point on the edge which we mark D. The corner A touches the opposite edge at a point which we mark C. Draw the line CD and cut along it with scissors. We get a new and special figure ABCD as in Figure 5.

Our last figure is a rectangle because all four angles are right angles. It is a rhombus because all four sides are equal. Check and see. Of course you already knew that this figure is a **square.** It is a special special parallelogram. Isn't it interesting that you knew the name for a square long before you ever heard of a parallelogram?

Still More Fun With a

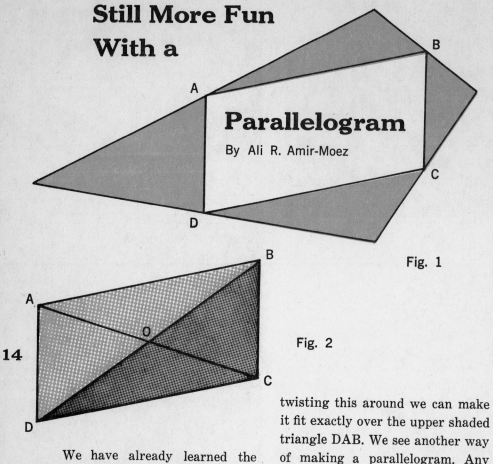

Parallelogram

By Ali R. Amir-Moez

Fig. 1

Fig. 2

14

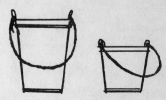
We have already learned the way to make a **parallelogram**. First we draw any four-sided figure or **quadrilateral** as the one made by the outer lines of Figure 1. We cut it out with scissors. We find the midpoints of each side by bringing its corners together and making a light crease at the middle of each side. We mark the midpoints A, B, C, and D. We connect the midpoints with lines as in Figure 1. We get a new special four-sided figure, a parallelogram.

Let's see what we can do with a parallelogram. First we draw the lines AC and BD as in Figure 2. The lines cross at a point called O. With a pencil, shade in differently the two parts on each side of line DB.

Then cut out the lower shaded triangle BCD. Notice that by twisting this around we can make it fit exactly over the upper shaded triangle DAB. We see another way of making a parallelogram. Any exactly equal triangles can be fitted together to make a parallelogram.

By comparing the triangles we can see that point O is just halfway between B and D and also just halfway between A and C. We could also say that the length of DO is equal to the length of OB. And the length of AO is equal to the length of OC.

Now let's make a puzzle. Cut out the upper shaded triangle DAB. And cut both triangles along the remaining lines AO and OC. This gives us four triangles. You will see that really there are two pairs of equal triangles. Each pair can be fitted together to make a new parallelogram.

You can arrange the four triangles in many different designs. How many designs can you make?

Another Parallelogram

By Ali R. Amir-Moez

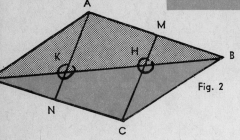

Fig. 1

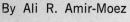

Fig. 2

We have learned how to make a *parallelogram* and how to cut it up to make a four-piece puzzle. Now let's make a six-piece puzzle which is still more fun.

We start by making a parallelogram just as we did before. First we draw ANY four-sided figure or quadrilateral, as the one made by the outer lines of Figure 1. We cut it out with scissors. We find the midpoints of each side by bringing its corners together and making a light crease in the middle. We mark the midpoints A, B, C, and D. Then we connect the midpoints with lines. We have a parallelo-

gram with corners at A, B, C, and D. We cut it out with scissors.

Now we are ready to make the puzzle. We find the middle of side AB by folding corner A over to corner B and making a light crease in the middle. We put a pencil mark at the edge and call it M. Likewise we find the midpoint of DC and call it N. Now we draw the lines DB, AN, and CM as in Figure 2. Where the lines cross there are two new points. Label them K and H and draw a rough circle around each of them. Now, with a pencil, shade in differently the two parts on each side of the line DB.

Your puzzle is now complete if it looks something like Figure 2. With scissors cut it out along the lines to give six pieces. Then put it back together so that it looks just

as it did before you cut it up.

Can you see that we did something special to the line DB? We cut it into three equal parts. Take out any one piece and compare its edge along DB with the other pieces. You will see that we cut the line DB into three equal parts DK, KH, and HB.

Maybe you can see what makes the puzzle so interesting. All six pieces have one side exactly alike. Really there are three pairs. Two pieces of each pair are exactly alike and will fit together to make a small parallelogram. Any two pairs of pieces will fit together to make a parallelogram. All six pieces will fit together in a new way to make a parallelogram. Try it and see. What other interesting designs can you make?

15

How Many Candles?

By Ali R. Amir-Moez

Here is a problem. Suppose we can only use two-thirds of each candle that we have because one-third of it goes inside the candlestick and is of no use to us. But whenever we collect three candle-ends, we can wax them together to make a new candle. If we have ten candle-ends, how many candles can we make?

Simon's answer was, "We can make three candles, and one candle-end will be left."

Aaron said, "No! We can make

four, and two candle-ends will be left."

Hannah remarked, "That's quite an improvement, but we can make five candles."

How did they figure their answers?

The first answer is easy. With nine of the ten candle-ends we can wax them together to make three candles, and one candle-end will be left.

But Aaron explained, "After we have used the three candles that we have made, then three more candle-ends will be left. So we make another candle. When we burn that one, we have another candle-end

left. So we have made four candles, and two candle-ends will be left."

"This is pretty good so far," said Hannah, "but now we can borrow a candle-end and, with the two candle-ends we already have, we make another candle. This way we have made five candles. When we have used this candle, we give back the candle-end that we have borrowed."

You can use this same idea to make up other kinds of problems. You can change the number of candle-ends that you have to start with. Or you can suppose that a candle-end is one-fourth or one-fifth of a candle. Try making up your own problem, then solve it.

Fun
With a Compass

By Ali R. Amir-Moez

The kind of compass we need here is a gadget for drawing a circle. Compasses come in different sizes and shapes but they really are much alike. Always there is a hinge between two arms of equal length. One arm has a sharp needle at the end. The other arm carries a pencil or a pen. A draftsman uses a very fancy compass. You can buy a simple one which will be just fine for what we want to do here.

We put the tip of the needle onto a paper at a point which will be the center of a circle. Then we swing the pencil arm slowly and carefully around without moving the needle from the center. We have drawn a circle.

All points on the circle are the same distance away from the center. This special distance, the **radius** of the circle, is also the distance between the needle and the tip of the pencil.

We also talk about the **diameter** which is always exactly two times as long as the radius of a circle. With a ruler draw a straight line which passes through the center and across the circle. Now you can see what is meant by the radius and the diameter of a circle.

You can make a smaller circle by squeezing the two arms of the compass together. Try it. You can make circles inside of circles inside of circles. You can also make all kinds of designs with circles which are even nicer when you color them. I have shown one of my designs but

I am sure you can make much better ones.

There are still more wonderful designs you can make with a compass, especially if you also use a pencil and ruler. And with crayons to add colors, your designs can be really fancy. Let's make a few together, and then you can take off on your own.

First draw a circle about four inches in diameter. Now be careful not to change the width of the compass arms. Put the needle at some point on the edge of the circle. With the pencil arm make a little mark across the circle. Then move the needle to the marked point and make another mark. Repeat this around the circle. We see that this is possible only six times and that we

16

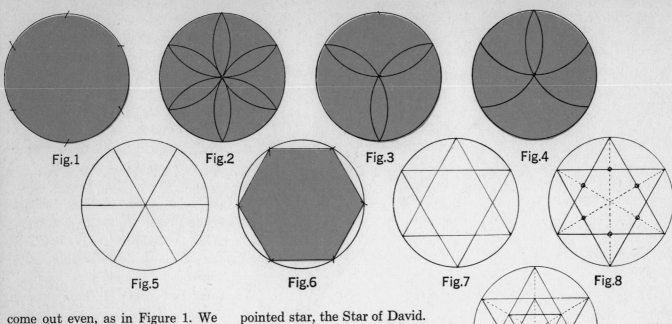

Fig.1 Fig.2 Fig.3 Fig.4

Fig.5 Fig.6 Fig.7 Fig.8

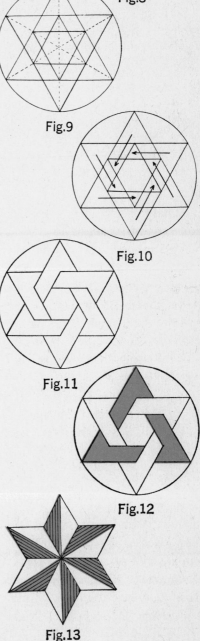

Fig.9

Fig.10

Fig.11

Fig.12

Fig.13

come out even, as in Figure 1. We have found a way to divide a circle into six equal parts. We have six points on the circle and the point made by the needle at the center. Now we can go.

Figure 2 is an easy design. We keep our compass set just as it was. We put the needle on each of our six points and draw the parts of circles which go inside the original circle. If we use just every other point, we can get the design of Figure 3. Or maybe you like better the design of Figure 4. How do we get that one?

Our designs can be even fancier if we use combinations of straight lines and circles. Each time, we start over again as in Figure 1. Suppose we draw straight lines from the center to each of the six points on the circle, as in Figure 5. This would be a way to cut a pie into six equal pieces.

Suppose we draw straight lines between the points next to each other. We get Figure 6. It is a **regular hexagon**, meaning a six-sided figure with equal sides and angles.

Suppose we draw straight lines to connect every other point, as in Figure 7. We get two overlapping triangles. Together these form a six-

pointed star, the Star of David.

We can erase the circle or some of the other lines to get new designs. Or we can add pieces to get combinations of designs.

Why don't you make one special design with me so you can see how fancy we can get? We will start with the Star of David as in Figure 7. We draw in dotted lines between opposite points of the star. This locates six new points which I have circled in Figure 8 just to show you where they are. We can use these points to make a second star inside of the first one, as in Figure 9.

Now we will erase the pieces of lines crossed by the arrows in Figure 10. We will also erase the dotted lines. We get a design of two triangles locked together as in Figure 11. Color or shade the two triangles differently. Then we get the design of Figure 12. Now erase the circle, and you can't even see that we used a compass. But it would have been pretty hard to do this design without one.

Can you see how I made the design of Figure 13?

I have shown you what can be done with a compass and ruler. Now you are on your own. Get a clean sheet of paper. See what designs you can dream up.

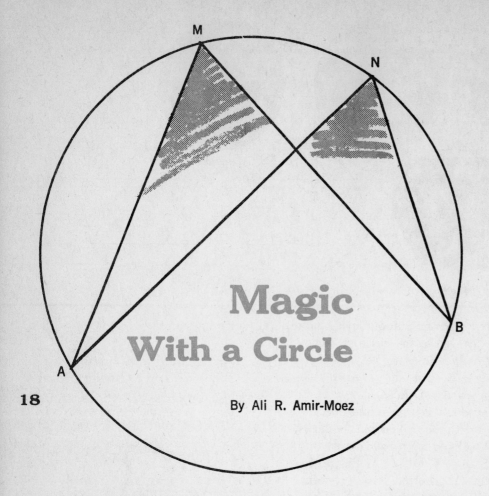

Magic
With a Circle

By Ali R. Amir-Moez

18

You have seen magic tricks with cards. The magician says, "Pick a card and remember what it is. Put it back in the deck. Now let's put the deck through this meat grinder. (Grind, grind.) Now I will chew up the deck and swallow it. (Chomp, chomp, and swallow, swallow.) And now here is your card. Isn't that amazing? I had it up my sleeve all the time."

Well, a circle can do magic for you without any sleeves. So let's go. Don't be a square. Draw a circle.

Here's trick No. 1: On the lower part of the circle put two points. Call them A and B.

Now choose any two points on the upper half of the circle. Or, to make a trick, get your father or mother to place the new points. Label them M and N. Draw straight lines connecting each lower point to both of the upper points. This gives the lines AM, AN, BM, and BN as shown in the illustration. It also gives us two special angles which we shade in with a pencil as in the illustration.

The tricky thing about the shaded angles at M and N is that they are just the same size. Cut out one with scissors, place it over the other one, and you will see. Wherever we place M and N on the upper part of the circle, the answer is always the same.

You may have to stop and think a little to see just how tricky this is. You have a circle with two points on the lower half. Now wherever you pick an upper point on the circle, the angle formed will always be the same size. How much more magical can you get?

In our second magic trick with a circle, we start just as we did in the first trick We draw a circle with a compass. We place two points on the lower half and call them A and B. Just to keep things straight it will help to draw a light line through points A and B.

Now we pick and choose. Pick any point on the upper piece or arc of the circle. Call it P. Pick another point on the lower arc of the circle and call it Q. Draw straight lines connecting A and B to each of these new points as in Figure 1.

Shade in the two special angles which you have formed and label the angles P and Q. The tricky thing about these angles is that they always can be fitted together to make a straight line as in Figure 2. Cut them out with scissors to try and see. The trick works, no matter where you pick P and Q—just so long as they are on opposite arcs.

The magic doesn't stop here. Something also is tricky about the angles with their points at A and B. Try this for yourself.

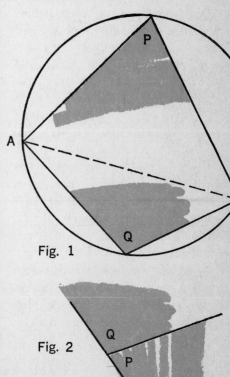

Fig. 1

Fig. 2

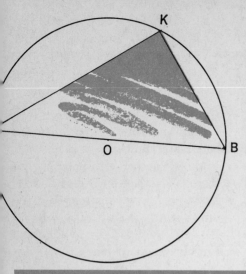

Here is our third magic trick with a circle. We draw it with a compass. The center of the circle we call O. Draw a straight line through this center so that it cuts the circle at two points. Call these two points A and B.

Now we pick and choose. Choose any point on the circle and label it K. Draw straight lines from K to A and to B. Shade in the angle which has its corner at K as in the illustration.

There is something special about the angle at K. It is a right angle as you can show by comparing it with the corner of a sheet of paper.

The trick is this. The angle at K will always be a right angle no matter where on the circle you choose to put point K. Try it and see.

Our fourth magic trick with a circle is more complicated. So it is more fun.

Draw a circle with a compass and call its center O. Mark two points on the circle and call them A and B. Draw straight lines from O to A and to B. We have formed an angle. Shade it in with a pencil as in the illustration. We can call it the angle with its tip or apex at O. Or we can call it angle AOB.

Now we pick and choose. Pick any new point on the big arc of the circle. Call it point P. Draw lines from P to A and to B. We have formed a new and special angle APB. Shade it in with pencil in some different way.

The second angle APB is special because it is just half as big as the first angle AOB. How can we prove this? With scissors, carefully cut out the shaded part of the first angle AOB. Now put the two sides together and make a crease down the center. The crease divides the angle exactly in half but with the tip still at O. Now that you have folded angle AOB exactly in half, place it on top of the second angle APB and compare. The tricky part is that this al-ways works, no matter where on the big arc you choose point P. You might like to think a little more about what we have done.

There are two other ways to start the same trick. We can start by drawing any angle. Call its tip point O. We want to make some new angle just half as big. First we draw a circle with its center at O. The circle will cross the sides of your angle at two points. Call these two points A and B. Now finish the trick just as you did before.

There is still one more way to start, but it is harder. Draw any small angle and call its tip P. Suppose we want to find a new angle twice as great. Look at the illustration. Pick up your compass. Now you figure it out.

19

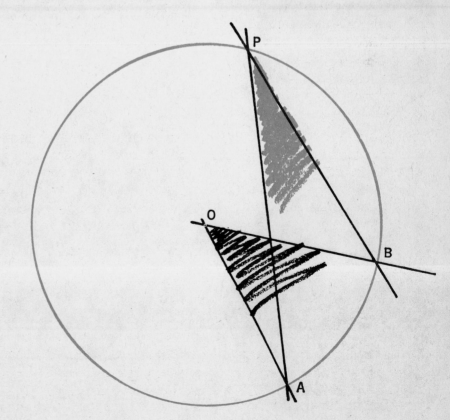

Circle, Square, Octagon

By Ali R. Amir-Moez

Draw and cut out a circle. Fold it in half and crease it. Open it, and mark the ends of the crease A and B. Now put point A on point B and fold the circle again. Mark the end points of the new crease C and D, Figure 1.

Connect A to C with a line, and C to B with another line. In the same way connect BD and DA. This forms a square. To test it, cut it out along lines AC, CB, BD, and DA. Then fold it several ways to find out if all sides are equal to one another, and all angles are right angles (that is, the same as a corner of a sheet of paper).

Now draw and cut out another circle. Fold and mark it as you did Figure 1. This time put point A on point C, and point D on point B. Fold the circle. Mark this new crease EF, Figure 2. What we have done here is find the middle of arc AC. This means that the part of the rim of the circle between A and

E will fit part of the rim of the circle between E and C.

Make another crease by folding the circle with A on D and C on B. Mark this new crease GH. Then draw the lines AE, EC, CG, GB, BF, FD, DH, and HA as in Figure 3. Cut out the figure along these lines. What you get is called a regular octagon—a flat figure with eight equal sides and eight equal angles. Test this figure by folding it in many different ways, comparing the sides and angles.

With Figure 3 as a base, you can make many other interesting objects. Make a new Figure 3 as before. This time connect every other point, Figure 4, to get an eight-point star.

With a new Figure 3 you can make another eight-point star, Figure 5. Describe how this is done.

There are ever so many other designs you can make by dividing up a circle. Happy designing to you!

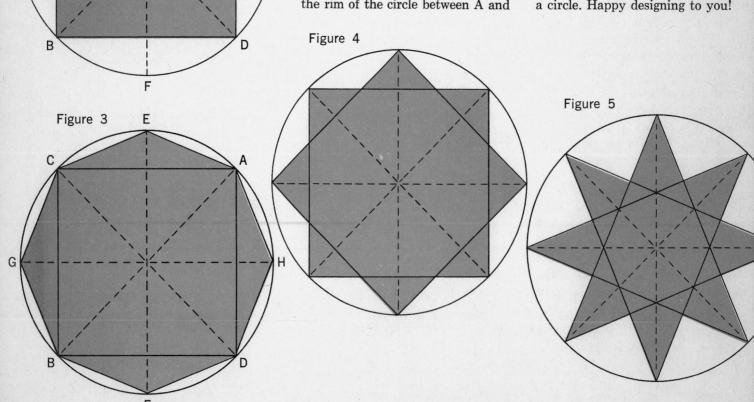

Figure 1

Figure 2

Figure 3

Figure 4

Figure 5

Construct a Cube

By Ali R. Amir-Moez

Let us first cut a square out of a sheet of paper. We call the corners of this sheet of paper P, Q, R, and S. We put the corner S on the side PQ and fold the paper so that the crease goes through the corner P. In the diagram we have shaded the part SQRM, Figure 1. This is the part that we cut from the paper, and we get a square.

Let us call the corners A, B, C, and D as in Figure 2. We fold this square by putting A on B and D on C. We get a crease. Again we fold the square by putting D on A and C on B. We get another crease. This way the original square has been divided into four equal squares.

For construction of a cube we need more squares so we have to fold the paper a few more times. We put D on H and C on K and fold the paper to make a new crease, Figure 3. Then we put A on H and B on K and fold the paper to make another crease.

We are sure that you can figure out how the other creases are made. Going from Figure 2 to Figure 3 is really dividing each small square into four equal squares. So we have sixteen squares. To construct a cube we have many choices.

We shall shade the parts that are to be cut, Figure 4. This way six squares which are connected to one another are left. We fold along all the edges which are between each two squares, Figure 5. Finally we use tape and put the loose edges together, Figure 6. What we get here is called a cube.

We can now say a cube has:

1. Six sides—all squares of the same size.

2. Twelve edges of the same size.

3. Eight corners.

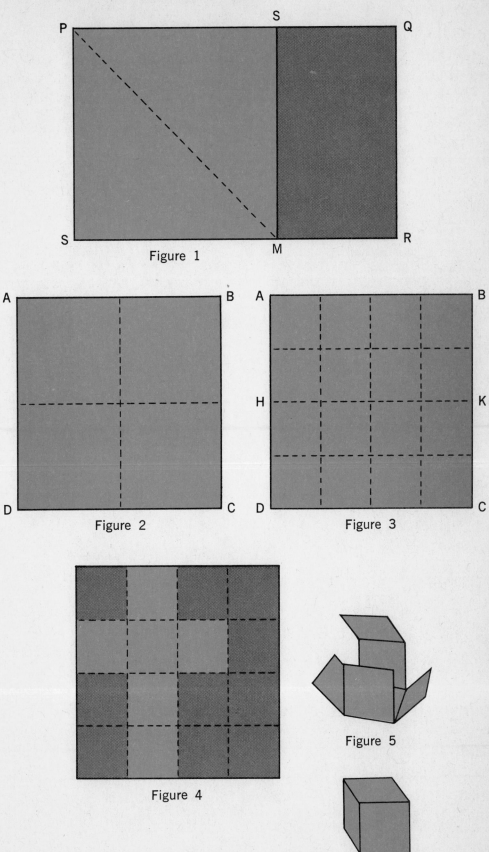

Figure 1

Figure 2

Figure 3

Figure 4

Figure 5

Figure 6

Clock Arithmetic By Ali R. Amir-Moez

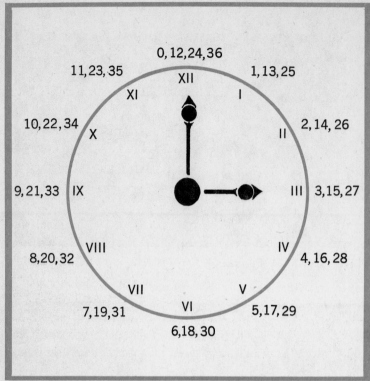

Figure 1

Figure 2

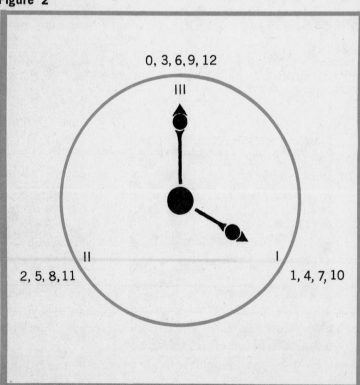

How do we add numbers which are written on a clock? For example, we ask: "It is nine o'clock. What will be seven hours later?"

The answer is not $9 + 7 = 16$, but $(9 + 7) — 12 = 4$. This is, indeed, an interesting kind of arithmetic. In fact this arithmetic plays an important part in mathematics. Let's do arithmetic with clock numbers. We will write all clock numbers with bars over them, like $\overline{5}$, so that we do not mistake clock numbers for ordinary numbers. Let's write an additional table for the arithmetic of clock numbers (Table I).

If we pick the clock number $\overline{9}$ across the top and the clock number $\overline{7}$ on the line at the left side, then we see that $\overline{9} + \overline{7} = \overline{4}$. In this addition $\overline{12}$ behaves like 0 (zero). For example, if it is five o'clock now, then 12 hours later it will again be five o'clock. This is like adding 0 to 5.

Now let us see what the numbers on the clock really stand for. The number $\overline{12}$ stands for zero hour, 12 noon, hour 24 or midnight, 12 hours later, and so on. In mathematics we write these numbers as a set of numbers such as:

$\overline{12} = \{\ldots, 0,12,24,36, \ldots\} = \text{XII}$

The number $\overline{1}$ stands for 1,13,25, and so on. This way we can write:

$\overline{1} = \{\ldots, 1,13,25, \ldots\} = \text{I}$

We can do this for the other clock numbers (Table II).

We can write these numbers on a clock, Figure 1. Each set is written next to what it means on the clock.

Now, just for fun, let's invent a new kind of clock. Suppose we make a clock with only three numbers as in Figure 2. Now we can

Table I

+	$\bar{1}$	$\bar{2}$	$\bar{3}$	$\bar{4}$	$\bar{5}$	$\bar{6}$	$\bar{7}$	$\bar{8}$	$\bar{9}$	$\overline{10}$	$\overline{11}$	$\overline{12}$
$\bar{1}$	$\bar{2}$	$\bar{3}$	$\bar{4}$	$\bar{5}$	$\bar{6}$	$\bar{7}$	$\bar{8}$	$\bar{9}$	$\overline{10}$	$\overline{11}$	$\overline{12}$	$\bar{1}$
$\bar{2}$	$\bar{3}$	$\bar{4}$	$\bar{5}$	$\bar{6}$	$\bar{7}$	$\bar{8}$	$\bar{9}$	$\overline{10}$	$\overline{11}$	$\overline{12}$	$\bar{1}$	$\bar{2}$
$\bar{3}$	$\bar{4}$	$\bar{5}$	$\bar{6}$	$\bar{7}$	$\bar{8}$	$\bar{9}$	$\overline{10}$	$\overline{11}$	$\overline{12}$	$\bar{1}$	$\bar{2}$	$\bar{3}$
$\bar{4}$	$\bar{5}$	$\bar{6}$	$\bar{7}$	$\bar{8}$	$\bar{9}$	$\overline{10}$	$\overline{11}$	$\overline{12}$	$\bar{1}$	$\bar{2}$	$\bar{3}$	$\bar{4}$
$\bar{5}$	$\bar{6}$	$\bar{7}$	$\bar{8}$	$\bar{9}$	$\overline{10}$	$\overline{11}$	$\overline{12}$	$\bar{1}$	$\bar{2}$	$\bar{3}$	$\bar{4}$	$\bar{5}$
$\bar{6}$	$\bar{7}$	$\bar{8}$	$\bar{9}$	$\overline{10}$	$\overline{11}$	$\overline{12}$	$\bar{1}$	$\bar{2}$	$\bar{3}$	$\bar{4}$	$\bar{5}$	$\bar{6}$
$\bar{7}$	$\bar{8}$	$\bar{9}$	$\overline{10}$	$\overline{11}$	$\overline{12}$	$\bar{1}$	$\bar{2}$	$\bar{3}$	$\bar{4}$	$\bar{5}$	$\bar{6}$	$\bar{7}$
$\bar{8}$	$\bar{9}$	$\overline{10}$	$\overline{11}$	$\overline{12}$	$\bar{1}$	$\bar{2}$	$\bar{3}$	$\bar{4}$	$\bar{5}$	$\bar{6}$	$\bar{7}$	$\bar{8}$
$\bar{9}$	$\overline{10}$	$\overline{11}$	$\overline{12}$	$\bar{1}$	$\bar{2}$	$\bar{3}$	$\bar{4}$	$\bar{5}$	$\bar{6}$	$\bar{7}$	$\bar{8}$	$\bar{9}$
$\overline{10}$	$\overline{11}$	$\overline{12}$	$\bar{1}$	$\bar{2}$	$\bar{3}$	$\bar{4}$	$\bar{5}$	$\bar{6}$	$\bar{7}$	$\bar{8}$	$\bar{9}$	$\overline{10}$
$\overline{11}$	$\overline{12}$	$\bar{1}$	$\bar{2}$	$\bar{3}$	$\bar{4}$	$\bar{5}$	$\bar{6}$	$\bar{7}$	$\bar{8}$	$\bar{9}$	$\overline{10}$	$\overline{11}$
$\overline{12}$	$\bar{1}$	$\bar{2}$	$\bar{3}$	$\bar{4}$	$\bar{5}$	$\bar{6}$	$\bar{7}$	$\bar{8}$	$\bar{9}$	$\overline{10}$	$\overline{11}$	$\overline{12}$

Table II

$\bar{2} = \{\ldots,\ 2,14,26,\ldots\} = \text{II}$

$\bar{3} = \{\ldots,\ 3,15,27,\ldots\} = \text{III}$

$\bar{4} = \{\ldots,\ 4,16,28,\ldots\} = \text{IV}$

$\bar{5} = \{\ldots,\ 5,17,29,\ldots\} = \text{V}$

$\bar{6} = \{\ldots,\ 6,18,30,\ldots\} = \text{VI}$

$\bar{7} = \{\ldots,\ 7,19,31,\ldots\} = \text{VII}$

$\bar{8} = \{\ldots,\ 8,20,32,\ldots\} = \text{VIII}$

$\bar{9} = \{\ldots,\ 9,21,33,\ldots\} = \text{IX}$

$\overline{10} = \{\ldots,\ 10,22,34,\ldots\} = \text{X}$

$\overline{11} = \{\ldots,\ 11,23,35,\ldots\} = \text{XI}$

write new sets of numbers which are simpler.

$\bar{3} = 0 = \{\ldots, 0,3,6,9,12,\ldots\} = \text{III}$

$\bar{1} = \{\ldots, 1,4,7,10,\ldots\} = \text{I}$

$\bar{2} = \{\ldots, 2,5,8,11,\ldots\} = \text{II}$

You can see that $\bar{3}$ now behaves like zero.

Here we write the addition table.

Table III

+	$\bar{1}$	$\bar{2}$	$\bar{3}$
$\bar{1}$	$\bar{2}$	$\bar{3}$	$\bar{1}$
$\bar{2}$	$\bar{3}$	$\bar{1}$	$\bar{2}$
$\bar{3}$	$\bar{1}$	$\bar{2}$	$\bar{3}$

Now we can ask whether we can do arithmetic with a clock having two numbers, four numbers, five numbers, and so on. Indeed, we can. Why don't you try several of them and write the addition table for each one.

23

An Accurate One-third   By Ali R. Amir-Moez

Judy was baby-sitting for three children on a rainy afternoon. Everything was quiet and the children were playing happily. All of a sudden a big argument started among them.

"What is the matter?" asked Judy.

Everyone talked at once, and Judy couldn't understand what was wrong. Calming everybody, she finally discovered that there was only one sheet of paper left, and all the children wanted to draw pictures.

"It would be very easy if there were two or four or eight children," thought Judy. "I could fold the paper once to divide it into two equal pieces, twice to divide it into four pieces, and so on. But what should I do now?"

This was a catastrophe! If the three pieces were not the same size, she would have trouble with the children. How should she solve the problem?

The solution is very easy. First, mark the corners of the paper A, B, C, and D. Then draw a diagonal line from corners B to D, or fold the paper and make a crease from corners B to D.

Now find the midpoint of AB by putting corner A on corner B and folding the paper. The crease gives the midpoint. Mark this midpoint M. The crease also gives the midpoint of DC. Mark this midpoint N.

With a ruler, draw lines AN and MC. These lines cut the diagonal DB at two points. Mark these points E and F.

Now fold the paper through point E, keeping point A on the line AB and point D on the line DC. Mark this crease PQ. Make a similar crease through point F. Mark this crease RS.

Cut the paper along PQ and along RS. If you have not made any mistakes, the three pieces of paper will be the same size. Test this by fitting one piece over another.

Possibilities and Probabilities

By Ali R. Amir-Moez

How many times have you heard someone say, "It is possible, but not probable?" Perhaps this expression has impressed you so much that you have been using it in its proper place, but really haven't understood it very well. Well, you are not the only one. I used to have trouble with it too until I looked at the meaning of the term **probability** more carefully.

Let us start with a very simple experiment. If you toss up a single coin, there are two possibilities for its fall—either it is heads or tails. Now, the chance of getting heads is one out of two. It is said that the probability of getting heads is one-half. Some people who compare most things with one hundred may say the probability of getting heads is fifty percent. Again, we may hear some people say there is a fifty-fifty chance of getting heads. So far we have learned four different ways of saying the same thing. But the expression used in a branch of mathematics called probability is: The probability of getting heads is $\frac{1}{2}$. There is only one head and only one tail. So we say the probability of getting heads is $\frac{1}{2}$; also the probability of getting tails is $\frac{1}{2}$.

Now let us see how we can make the idea more interesting. Choose two coins; for example, a dime and a nickel. Toss up both. Now count very carefully all possible ways they may land.

1. Both coins are heads.
2. The dime is heads and the nickel is tails.
3. The dime is tails and the nickel is heads.
4. Both coins are tails.

We see that there are four, and only four, **possibilities**. The **probability** of getting both coins heads is $\frac{1}{4}$; that is, the chance of one out of four. The probability of getting a head and a tail is $2/4$ or $\frac{1}{2}$. But if we ask what the probability of getting heads for the dime and tails for the nickel is, the answer is $\frac{1}{4}$. Why?

Suppose you have a bowl of candies wrapped in paper so that you cannot see what flavor the candy is. If the bowl contains half lemon candies and half cherry candies, what is the probability of your picking out a lemon candy?

If the bowl contains 100 candies, 25 each of lemon, cherry, peppermint, and butterscotch, what is the probability of getting a lemon candy?

Using a chart like the one shown, record the results of taking a candy out of the bowl 40 times. Did you get about 10 lemons? If you had a giant bowl of 10,000 candies, and drew out 1,000, you would be even more likely to get 1 lemon for every 4 candies picked out.

Now think about the probability of getting either a lemon or a cherry candy out. What is the probability of getting one of these two each time you draw out a candy? The same rule of probability applies as in the coin-tossing experiment.

What's Your Favorite Number?

Here's a good number trick. You don't even have to be good at arithmetic to do it. Say to a friend, "Write all the numbers from 1 to 9 across on a line." His line of figures will look like this:

1 2 3 4 5 6 7 8 9.

Now ask him, "Which is your favorite number?" If he says 2, tell him to multiply the row of numbers by his favorite number. This is what will happen:

```
  1 2 3 4 5 6 7 8 9
              x 2
  2 4 6 9 1 3 5 7 8
```

Now tell him to multiply that answer by 9. And this is how it will turn out:

```
  2 4 6 9 1 3 5 7 8
              x 9
  2 2 2 2 2 2 2 0 2
```

Except for the one zero, there is a whole row of his favorite number! It doesn't matter which number he picks as his favorite. This trick will work with any number. Remember these steps: 1. Write the numbers 1 to 9 in a row. 2. Multiply by your favorite number. 3. Multiply the answer by 9.

Selected by: Mary Ann Durbin
Delta, Ohio

More Possibilities and Probabilities

By Ali R. Amir-Moez

In experimenting with two coins we found there are four possible ways in which a dime and a nickel can show heads and tails.

Now let us take one more step. We will choose three coins: a dime, a nickel, and a penny. When we toss them up, each coin can fall heads or tails. How many possible combinations of heads and tails are there for the three coins?

Counting all the possibilities now is more difficult. We can find them if we arrange the coins in order and carefully make all the combinations one by one. Here they are:

1. All coins are heads.
2. Dime is heads, nickel is heads, penny is tails.
3. Dime is heads, nickel is tails, penny is heads.
4. Dime is tails, nickel is heads, penny is heads.
5. Dime is heads, nickel is tails, penny is tails.
6. Dime is tails, nickel is heads, penny is tails.
7. Dime is tails, nickel is tails, penny is heads.
8. All coins are tails.

These are the only possible combinations in which the three coins can fall. And in any one toss each combination has the same chance. Notice 2, 3, and 4. There are three different ways in which we can get two heads and one tails. And notice 5, 6, and 7. There are three different ways in which we can get one heads and two tails. The chance of getting all heads is one out of eight, so we can say that the probability of all heads is ⅛. The probability of two heads and one tails is ⅜. What is the probability of all tails? What is the probability of one heads and two tails?

Now let's look at an interesting arrangement of certain numbers. For only one coin we have the possibilities: 1 heads and 1 tails. For two coins we have: 1 all heads, 2 with one heads and one tails, and 1 all tails. For three coins we have: 1 all heads, 3 with two heads and one tails, 3 with one heads and two tails, 1 all tails. We write these numbers in a triangular form as:

one coin		1 1	
two coins		1 2 1	
three coins		1 3 3 1	

At the ends of each row of numbers we find 1. Except for the 1's, each number is found by adding the two numbers directly above it. If we continue the idea, we may write the row of numbers for four coins. We start with the row for three coins (as above). Under and between 1 and 3 we write 4. Under and between 3 and 3 we write 6. Under and between 3 and 1 we write 4. Then we put 1's at each end:

```
  1  3  3  1
1  4  6  4  1
```

This last line happens to be all the possibilities corresponding to four coins. That is, for four coins— a quarter, a dime, a nickel, and a penny—we get:

1. One way of getting all heads.
2. Four ways of getting 3 heads, 1 tails.
3. Six ways of getting 2 heads, 2 tails.
4. Four ways of getting 1 heads, 3 tails.
5. One way of getting all tails.

Now you can figure out the probabilities for each of these combinations.

We will add one more row of numbers to the triangle to give

```
      1  1
     1  2  1
    1  3  3  1
   1  4  6  4  1
  1  5 10 10  5  1
```

and then you can go on adding more rows at the bottom as far as you wish.

This arrangement of numbers is called a Pascal Triangle. Pascal, a seventeenth century scientist, used the Triangle in working out a mathematical theory for games of chance. The idea, however, is quite old and can be found in a book written by the Persian mathematician Al-Khowarizimi back in the ninth century.

25

"I'm five. How old are you?"

The Magic of Zero

By Linda Myers

Every day you see or work with numbers. You need them to count or to read a clock or a calendar. You need them to make change when you buy something. And you work with numbers at school. So let's think about our system of numbers. It really is a clever system.

Let's start by counting: 1, 2, 3, 4, 5, 6, 7, 8, 9, 10. . . . Hold it right there! You already have used all the symbols or digits you will ever use, no matter how high you count. And what are these digits? You may think this is a silly question, but stop and look at them again. Really there are ten digits: 0, 1, 2, 3, 4, 5, 6, 7, 8, and 9. By putting these together in the right way, you can keep counting to as big a number as you can think of. And how about zero? Why do you need a zero when it means nothing at all? Before we can answer that we must see how our number system works.

Nowadays, all over the world, most people use the same system of numbers that you and I use. But it was not always this way.

The Roman system of numbers was used in the Roman Empire and was still used in Europe almost to the time of Christopher Columbus. It had different symbols and different rules. Letters were used for numbers. I=1, V=5, X=10, L=50, C=100, D=500, M=1000. You count like this: I, II, III, IV, V, VI, VII, VIII, IX, X. With just three symbols, I, V, X, you can count to 49. It is easy to see that II stands for two, III stands for three, and IV stands for five minus one, or four.

The Roman system was easy to use for small numbers—and in those days no one needed very big numbers. But advanced arithmetic was not so easy. Multiplying and dividing were so difficult that they were taught only in universities.

Our number system grew up in India and the Middle East and is often called the Hindu-Arabic system. It is really very much better than the Roman system. The basic idea is that the value of a digit depends upon where it is in a number, its position or **place.** Now let's see just how our number system works.

Pick a nice number like 3333. Let's take it apart to see what it really means. We will write its digits in a frame with boxes or places marked by letters.

D	C	B	A
3	3	3	3

The 3 in place A has a value of 3, but the 3 in place B is worth ten times more—it has a value of 30. The value of 3 in place C is 300, ten times more than it has in place B. And in place D the 3 has a value

again ten times more—now it is worth 3000. We can see that the value of each 3 depends upon where it is.

There are other ways of writing 3333 that show the idea of place. We can write it as three thousand, three hundred and thirty-three, or $3000 + 300 + 30 + 3$. There is still another way used by mathematicians which tells even more about the idea of place in our number system.

In multiplication there is a special case in which we multiply a number by itself. This happens often enough that we have a special way of writing it. Think of 6×6. This can be written also as 6^2 which is read as "6 to the power of 2" or "6 squared." The little ^{2} up above is called the power because it tells the number of 6's that are to be multiplied together. Just so you will understand what comes later, you should notice that 6^1 is just the same as 6. So we do not bother to show a power unless it is different from ^{1}.

We use this same idea for higher powers. $4^3 = 4 \times 4 \times 4$ and is read "4 raised to third power" or "4 cubed." Or $7^4 = 7 \times 7 \times 7 \times 7$ and is read "7 raised to the fourth power." Also $10^5 = 10 \times 10 \times 10 \times 10 \times 10 = 100,000$ and we could read it as "10 raised to the fifth power."

Notice that, of the different numbers we have tried, 10 is a special one. It is easy to figure the answer for any power of 10. Multiplying by 10 just adds a zero, doesn't it? A power of 10 like ^{5} in 10^5 shows the number of zeros which follow the 1. So 10^5 is 100,000. Pretty slick, isn't it?

Now let's go back to the number

26

3333. We can also write it

3000 + 300 + 30 + 3

or

$3 \times 1000 + 3 \times 100 + 3 \times 10 + 3 \times 1$

or

$3 \times 10^3 + 3 \times 10^2 + 3 \times 10 + 3 \times 1$

We started out using letters to show the different places. Now we can see that the places are really represented by 10 raised to various powers.

Perhaps you can see now why 10 is a special number. It is special because it was chosen as the **base** of our number system. When we say that we use the **base 10** we mean that we count in groups of tens. In counting, whenever we get past nine we are finishing a group. So we add one in the column to the left and start over with a zero.

Think of .. 8, 9, 10 .. or .. 28, 29, 30 ..

Now it is time to think again about that zero. We have seen that our Hindu-Arabic system of numbers is really a place system. The value of a digit depends upon what place it is in. You know that 765 and 7605 and 7650 are different numbers. Without a zero how could we tell? We need some way to show that in 7605 we are not using the x 10 place and in 7650 we are not using the x 1 place. Of course we could always write our numbers in frames like

7	6		5

but that would be clumsy.

Now you see why the idea of zero was one of the great inventions of all time. We need it to make the place system work. Because of zero we can show the place and value of each digit without using a frame. With the ten symbols 1, 2, 3, 4, 5, 6, 7, 8, 9, and a 0 to stand for "none" we can count just as high as we wish.

You should know that 10 is not the only possible base for a number system. We just happen to use the base 10. A very long time ago people counted on their fingers—just as you did when you were learning to count. And it just happens that most people have ten fingers. Actually, we could use any old number like 4 or 7 for a base.

How Big Is An Acre?

"Did you buy it, Dad? Where is it? How big is it?" The children were crowding around their father who was just back from a trip.

"Yes, I bought it. It is a lot with trees and a good place to build a cabin someday. The lot is on Long Lake where we stopped to fish last summer. It is supposed to be just about an acre in size."

"How big is an acre?" asked Mike.

"Well, I have seen the lot, so

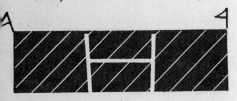

I know. But I don't know quite how to tell you. Let's see what the dictionary says."

Patsy ran for the big dictionary and rustled through the pages to find "acre." "Here it is. It says, 'A measure of land, originally the amount plowed by a yoke of oxen in one day.' "

Dad joined in the laughter. "That won't help much. I don't think we could get a yoke of oxen to find out. What else does it say?"

"It says that an acre is 160 square rods."

"That doesn't help much, either. I have forgotten how long a rod is."

"It also says that an acre is 43,560 square feet."

"Now we are getting closer. What can we think of that might be that big? How about a tennis court or a baseball diamond or a football field? Look up and see how big a football field is."

So Patsy thumbed through the big dictionary again. "Why, our dictionary even has diagrams. The English and American football fields are different. Our kind is 160 feet across and 300 feet long."

"Let's see how many square feet that would be. Tommy, why don't you get a pencil and paper and figure it out?"

Tommy multiplied 300 feet times 160 feet. "This is like a problem in my homework. It comes out 48,000 square feet. That is a little more than an acre."

"Well, there you are," said Dad. "Of course our lot is not shaped quite like a football field. Actually it is shaped more like a piece of pie. But it must have almost as much land as a football playing field.

"I'm glad you asked the question, Mike. Now we have an idea about how big an acre really is."

How To Count Like a Big Computer

By Donald H. Menzel

You have heard about computers. They are big electrical machines that work ever so fast. You can give one of those machines a very hard problem, push a few buttons, and out will come the answer printed on a card or piece of paper. It might be fun to have one help you with your arithmetic. But don't be so sure. Actually, computers are not so very bright. They are just fast.

Computers are used to do very complicated arithmetic. They really do this in the simplest possible ways. For example, instead of multiplying a number by two they just add the number to itself. But they do this very rapidly. In a single day one computer can do more work than a thousand men could do in ten years with pencil and paper.

One thing a computer can do is count. It can count $1 + 1 + 1 + 1 + 1 + 1 + 1 + 1 + 1 + 1 + 1 + 1 + 1 + 1 + 1 + 1 = 17$ faster than you can blink an eye. In fact it can count to over a million while you are saying, "One, two, three." We are going to learn to count in the way that a computer does it.

A really surprising thing about computers is that they use only two numbers, one and zero. It may sound silly but we can make a very good number system this way—especially for a computer. Before we see how the computer's number system works, let's think about the number system we use. With the figures or numerals 1, 2, 3, 4, 5, 6, 7, 8, 9, and 0, we can write any number, large or small. To write any number, we need to put the figures together in a proper order.

Because we count in groups of tens, a table of 10's is easy. For example:

$$1 = 1$$
$$10 \times 1 = 10$$
$$10 \times 10 = 100$$
$$10 \times 100 = 1000$$
$$10 \times 1000 = 10,000$$
$$10 \times 10,000 = 100,000$$ and so on.

Each time we multiply by 10, we just write a zero after the number, like $10 \times 243 = 2430$.

When we write a number like 3764, the way we write the figures down has a special meaning. The arrangement means that this number contains:

$$3000 \text{ or } 3 \times 10 \times 10 \times 10 = 3 \times 1000$$
$$+ 700 \text{ or } 7 \times 10 \times 10 = 7 \times 100$$
$$+ 60 \text{ or } 6 \times 10 = 6 \times 10$$
$$+ 4 \text{ or } 4 = 4 \times 1$$

The number 3764 means:

Thousands	Hundreds	Tens	Ones
3	7	6	4

The value of any one figure in a number depends upon its position or **place.**

We can say that our usual number system is a **decimal** system because it counts in groups of tens. We can also say that it is a **place** system because we let the place of a figure tell us how many ones or tens or hundreds or thousands it stands for.

We can make the place system work with groups of numbers other than ten. The smallest group we can use is two. Then we need only two figures, one and zero. This will give the system which computers use—the **binary** system.

We are going to use the binary system and do arithmetic like a computer does it. In order to remember what system we are using, let us use a new kind of figure like "T" to stand for one. We shall use "0" to stand for zero just as it usually does.

In the binary system we are going to use the idea of place just as we always do, but we are going to use groups based on two. So now when we add a zero after a number we will be multiplying it by two—not by ten. In Table I, you will see the easy numbers written out in both systems.

Notice that $2 = \text{T}0$. It's easy to remember. Pronounce it. "T0" says "Two." Now look at one of the big numbers like 512, for example. $512 = 2 \times 2 \times 2 \times 2 \times 2 \times 2 \times 2 \times 2 \times 2$, or 2 multiplied by itself 9 times. So there are nine zeros after the T for the number 512.

Now let's write some number like 721 in the binary system. We will use the numbers in the table to find the simplest combination which adds up to 721. We do it this way. The largest number less than 721 is 512. So 721—512 = 209 left over. The largest number less than 209 is 128. So 209—128 = 81 left over. And we go on the same way. 81—64 = 17. And 17 —16 = 1. We have broken down 721 into numbers we know in the binary system. 721 = 512 + 128 + 64 + 16 + 1. Now we just add them up.

$$
\begin{array}{rcl}
\text{T000000000} &=& 512 \\
\text{T0000000} &=& 128 \\
\text{T000000} &=& 64 \\
\text{T0000} &=& 16 \\
\text{T} &=& 1 \\
\hline
\text{T0TT0T000T} &=& 721
\end{array}
$$

In Table II you will see the first 32 numbers written in both systems. Try counting in the binary system to see how it works.

To add in the binary system we need to remember only three combinations.

Binary	Decimal
0 + 0 = 0	0 + 0 = 0
T + 0 = T	1 + 0 = 1
T + T = T0	1 + 1 = 2

Try adding some simple numbers.

$$
\begin{array}{rr}
\text{T0} & 2 \\
+\text{T} & +1 \\
\hline
\text{TT} & 3
\end{array}
$$

Next add TT + T. We will add two T's, getting T0, and then carry the T to the next column:

$$
\begin{array}{rr}
\text{TT} & 3 \\
+\text{T} & +1 \\
\hline
\text{T00} & 4
\end{array}
$$

Try adding 9 and 19.

$$
\begin{array}{rr}
\text{T00TT} & 19 \\
+\text{T00T} & +9 \\
\hline
\text{TTT00} & 28
\end{array}
$$

Now you know how to count and add in the binary number system. In another article we will learn to do more arithmetic in the binary system—the way a computer does.

Table I

Binary Style	Decimal Style			
T				1
T0	2	×	1 =	2
T00	2	×	2 =	4
T000	2	×	4 =	8
T0000	2	×	8 =	16
T00000	2	×	16 =	32
T000000	2	×	32 =	64
T0000000	2	×	64 =	128
T00000000	2	×	128 =	256
T000000000	2	×	256 =	512
T0000000000	2	×	512 =	1024

Table II

Binary	Decimal
0	0
T	1
T0	2
TT	3
T00	4
T0T	5
TT0	6
TTT	7
T000	8
T00T	9
T0T0	10
T0TT	11
TT00	12
TT0T	13
TTT0	14
TTTT	15
T0000	16
T000T	17
T00T0	18
T00TT	19
T0T00	20
T0T0T	21
T0TT0	22
T0TTT	23
TT000	24
TT00T	25
TT0T0	26
TT0TT	27
TTT00	28
TTT0T	29
TTTT0	30
TTTTT	31
T00000	32

29

The Binary System

The fruit cart at the left shows how the decimal system of counting is used.

The cart on the right has the fruit marked at the same price but in the binary system. Can you figure out how to write the price of apples using the binary system?

Let's Talk About Computers

By Roy Johnson
Program Manager
Honeywell Information Systems, Inc.

How fast can you add ten numbers together and get the right answer? In ten seconds? That's pretty fast. But did you know that in ten seconds a modern digital computer can add over one million numbers?

It is this great speed which makes computers so valuable. In hours they work problems which would take men whole lifetimes to solve by hand. Because they can solve all kinds of problems, computers have come to be used in many ways. Banks use them to keep their accounts. Airlines use them to keep track of tickets. Big stores use them to keep track of materials on hand. Scientists use them to solve problems so complicated that they could never have been tackled before. They are used to control space flights. In fact, without their lightning calculations, no one could keep an 18,000-mile-an-hour rocket on just the right path.

The computer is a wonderful machine for doing arithmetic. Let's see if we can get some idea about how it works.

The computer uses a number system very much simpler than the one we commonly use. In counting and doing arithmetic, you and I use the **decimal** system which has ten symbols or digits: 0, 1, 2, 3, 4, 5, 6, 7, 8, 9. We can put them together to represent any number we want. If a computer were to use the decimal system, it would need electronic circuits which could represent each of these ten different digits.

Suppose that we just have one electronic circuit. We can easily

The inside of a modern computer.

make it work so that it sends an electric current or it doesn't send one. If the current is on, it can represent one digit like 1. If the current is off, that represents another digit like 0. Now there is a number system which uses just two digits, 1 and 0. It is called the **binary** system. We can count just as high and do arithmetic just as well in the binary system as in the decimal system. As you learned, we can write any number in the binary system by putting down 1's and 0's (or T's and 0's) in the right combination. For example, 110 in the binary system stands for the number 6 in our usual decimal system.

Now you see why the binary system is so good for computers. A pulse of electric current means 1. No pulse at all means 0. With electronic circuits we can make the pulses of electric current count and do arithmetic. And since electricity travels

so fast, a computer can work with numbers ever so much faster than your brain.

In the computer a group of 1's and 0's can be used to represent not only numbers but also other information like instructions and letters of the alphabet. A group of 1's and 0's is called a **word**. And each of the 1's and 0's of a word is called a **bit**. Usually a computer does all its work using a certain size word. Some computers use a 32-bit word. Inside such a computer the number 6 would look like this:

00000000 00000000 00000000 00000110

Besides being able to work with numbers, the computer needs something else you have in your brain. It needs a **memory**. To have a memory, you need a way of storing away information and then being able to get it back. Even though we don't know just how it works, your brain does this very well. Long ago you stored away the information that the word **CAT** stands for kitty-cat. In fact you stored away the meaning of most of the words on this page. Otherwise you would not understand what you are reading.

The computer does not have a brain, but it does have a memory. It uses millions of special electronic memory circuits. Each circuit can be given a tiny electric charge, or can have its charge removed. If the circuit is charged, it remembers a 1. If it is not charged, it remembers a 0. Since each circuit can remember one bit of a binary word, it takes 32 circuits to remember a 32-bit word. In a modern computer 16,000 bits of memory can be stored on the chip shown on this page. The largest computers have enough memory circuits to store several million words. A computer can store a word in its memory or take a word out of memory in less than a millionth of a second.

We have seen that a computer can do arithmetic and that it has a memory. This makes it seem pretty smart. But the computer cannot really think. Before it can solve a problem, a human being must break the problem down into simple steps which the computer can do, one at a time. Each of these steps is called an **instruction**. And the whole list of instructions is called a **program**.

After a program is figured out, we must somehow "tell" it to the computer. The most common way to do this is to type it on a special typewriterlike device called a "terminal," which is connected to the computer. Another way is to punch holes in cards to represent the instructions of the program. The cards are put into a "card reader" which sends to the computer groups of 1's and 0's which represent instructions. Each instruction is put into memory. In the computer's memory an instruction might look like this:

10011111 11111111 11011011 00000111

To the computer the combination of 1's and 0's in each instruction means a certain task to be done. For example, an instruction may tell the computer to take a number from memory, add it to another number, and put the answer in a certain word in memory.

When working on a problem, the computer takes instructions from memory one at a time. When one instruction is completed, the computer doesn't stop to "think" what to do next—as you and I would. It goes right on to the next instruction from memory and does the next step. As they zip along most computers have tiny lights blinking on and off to let the operator know they are working happily. And when the instructions are all done, the problem is solved.

There are different ways in which a computer can give back its final answer to problems. One way is that it types the answer on a terminal. Another is that it prints the answer on a strip of paper, using a high-speed printer.

Some of the really big computers cost several million dollars. And just the use of one may cost several hundred dollars an hour. So someone must do a lot of thinking about a problem and make up a good program before a computer ever goes to work. For a computer is only as smart as the person who knows how to tell it what to do.

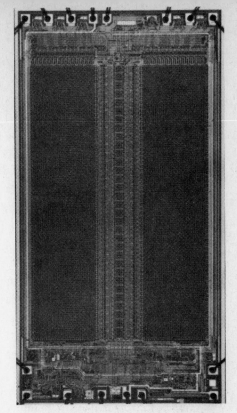

This is a memory circuit chip that has 16,000 memory circuits. This picture has been magnified; the chip is really this big ▮ .

In the last article (page 28) Dr. Menzel used the symbols 0 and T in order to help you remember that you were working with the binary system. In this article the author uses the symbols 0 and 1 which are more common. You will see that you can pick any two symbols you like to stand for the two digits of the binary system.

Inside a computer room. All these units together make up what is called a "data-processing system."

31

How To Do Arithmetic Like a Big Computer

By Donald H. Menzel

We have learned to count and add in the binary system—the number system which computers use. Let's see how it works.

We let "0" stand for zero, just as it usually does. We could let "1" stand for one. But it is easier if we let "T" stand for one. This helps us remember that we are using a special number system.

We have only two digits, so we count in groups of twos. In Table I you will see the easy numbers written out in both systems. In Table II you can see all the numbers up to 32.

Now that we have learned to count, let's go right on and do more

arithmetic. It won't be easy. If you don't like to think, stop right here. If you do like to think and struggle a little with your mind, this will be fun.

The best thing about doing arithmetic in the binary system is that it is easy to remember the rules.

To add in the binary system, we need to remember only three combinations.

Binary	Decimal
0 + 0 = 0	0 + 0 = 0
T + 0 = T	1 + 0 = 1
T + T = T0	1 + 1 = 2

Try adding some simple numbers.

T0	2
+T	+1
TT	3

Next add TT + T. We will add two T's, getting T0, and then carry the T to the next column:

TT	3
+T	+1
T00	4

Try adding 9 and 19:

T00TT	19
+T00T	+9
TTT00	28

Multiplication is simple. All we have to learn is a table of "ones."

Binary	Decimal
0 × 0 = 0	0 × 0 = 0
T × 0 = 0	1 × 0 = 0
T × T = T	1 × 1 = 1

Suppose we want to multiply some number by 19 which is T00TT. We break it into its binary parts, T + T0 + 000 + 0000 + T0000. Now T times any number equals the number itself. T0 times any number is that number with

a zero added. And T0000 times a number adds four zeros. Suppose we wish to multiply 25 × 19. 25 = TT00T.

TT00T x T =		TT00T	25 x 1 = 25
TT00T x T0 =		TT00T0	25 x 2 = 50
		T00T0TT	75
		T00T0TT	75
TT00T x T0000 =	TT00T0000	25 x 16 = 400
		TTT0TT0TT	475

We can check the final answer by breaking it up:
TTT0TT0TT = 256 + 128 + 64 + 0 + 16 + 8 + 0 + 2 + 1 = 475.

Division is almost as simple as multiplication. We subtract in steps instead of adding. For subtraction we use the rules:

Binary	Decimal
0 − 0 = 0	0 − 0 = 0
T − 0 = T	1 − 0 = 1
T − T = 0	1 − 1 = 0
0 − T = ?	0 − 1 = ?

To do this last subtraction, we have to borrow a T from the column to the left. So in subtracting 2 − 1 = 1, we can write T0 − T = T.

Now suppose we want to divide 475 by 19, the reverse of the problem we just did. We will do our division by subtracting and keeping track of each step. Write down the binary number for 475. Under it write the binary number for 19 so that the left-hand columns line up. Now put enough zeros after the 19 to fill up the columns. You will see that we will have to add four zeros to T00TT. We are really multiplying it by 2 four times, so it becomes 19 × 16.

(1)

TTT0TT0TT		475
−T00TT0000	19 × 16 =	304
T0T0T0TT		171

For our second step we take the remainder and repeat in the same